Meself and me Mummy wood luffs to
dedicates this booky to all ours sooper fambly
and frends and fanks them for all thems
helpyness and thems hencurragements and
for doing me lunchtime wees.

Me Moosings: Moosings of a 'tired Greyhound

Written by Becky Carr

Designed and produced by Nicki Porter - www.mrspcreative.co.uk

Published by Diverze Publishing - www.diverze-publishing.com

First Edition - Printed 2013 in Great Britain by Diverze Print - www.diverze-print.com

Me Moosings

Moosings of a 'tired Greyhound

by Davids Best Mate

The Beginnings

As I do layings here in me warm, cumfy nest bed wiv me duck and chewing on a sosidge, I remembers wot it woz like wen I woz back being an afleet doing me trayning and me runnings and winnings and I duz wundering how I did eva gets a desent snooze. I did luffs me runnings, speshally me winnings becoz I did gets sooper hooge trowfies ands fings but insted of a sooper cumfy nest bed we did snoozing in our kennels on papers and we didn't hav any ducks.

I woz borned in Eye-land back in too-fowsand-and-too and did start me trayning to do runnings sooper fast ova there wiv me bruvvas and sistas. Wen I woz a puppy, before I did hav me proper name, the hoo-mans did calls meself Elvis. Meself and me bruvvas and sistas wood wakes hup, havs brekfst (me favrit), plays chase wivs ourselfs, annoy ours muvva (who wood sumtimes do snap snap grr to keeps us being sensible and polite puppies and I wood put me Good Boy Puppy Ears on becoz I did even hav them wen I woz little) and then hav a snooze or too. As we did getting a bit more older we wood goes out to practiss chasing wabbits to get sooper qwik. I woz sooper good at me runnings. Wen I woz good enuff, I did gets me proper name 'David's Best Mate' and me tattoos in me ears, wot did makes meself feel likes a proper grow'd hup racings hound, just likes me farva! To furver me racings career I needed to do travling away from me fambly to Inglund to do racings proply. It woz sooper hexcitings. We did goes in the tiny starting boxes wiv you's competitors beside you. Then you did heering the bell and you did runs after the wabbit as fast as wot you cood (I duz luffs wabbits). I did do racings ova sebenty times and winnings sooper lots! After we had dunned our runnings we did go back to ours kennels for dinners and a snooze, becoz afleets needs to do millyons of snoozings to keeps thems energies hup.

That did be's until I did hurtings me leg. One day, wen I woz racings sooper fast, I did feels a pop ins me back leg and it didn't do workings proply. I did the Greyhound Screem ofs Deff becoz it mite havs felled off compleetlies. I had to do me limpies limpies until me trainer did

Doing me running! I's in bloo!

Me foto froms me job hadvert in the paper for being a companyon

cort meself and taked meself to the vetandhairy man. The vetandhairy man see'd to meself and shaked hims hed. Hims sez 'I's sorries David's Best Mate, but you's racing days is ova'. Me trayner sed to meself it did be okies tho becoz thems wood send meself to a noo kennels where thems cood find meself a noo job to do, not as a profeshonal afleet but as a 'tired companyon.

The hole fing did be a sooper wurry becoz, at only for years old, I's neva be'd a companyon befores. I didn't no's wot I wood need to do, or if it did hinvolve wabbits (becoz thems woz me favrit) or snoozings becoz even afleets wot isn't afleets anymore need snoozings!

So there I did be's in the noo kennels waytings to finds sumone wot wanted a'not-good-enuff-to-be-an-afleet-anymores' hound to works as a companyon for them. A few weeks afta settlings in I did goes on a trip to see's a different vetandhairy man. Hims looked meself all ova, sed I woz qwite hansum and in sooper good shape. Hims looked in me mouf and did sez 'fwor, you's breff duz stinking'. Charmings! Thems did gives meself a sharp ins me leg and suddenly I woz feeling qwite sleepies. I duz luffs a snooze so I did laying down. Befores I did no it I woz awakes agen but me legs did feel sooper sillies so I did hav anuvva snooze. Heventually, I did wakes hup and finked 'I can't do remembering the last time I did cleen me boys bits' so did goes about havings a bit of a wash of them ands... ANDS... you will neva gess wot! Too of me boys bits had gonned! Gonned completelies! Sumone sneekies had stolled them wen I woz snoozing! Fankfullies thems had not stolled me himportant boys bit wot is used for wee-mayls becoz that wood be's terribles!

As I woz waytings in me kennel for me noo job to comes along, a hound called Alan did comes back to kennels for hims hollydays afta having a job as a companyon for a little wile. Alan did tellings us abouts sofas and dooveys and leff-dovers and bed snuggles wivs hoomans. We did all gavverings round wen hims woz telling us about hims noo life. Hims telled us about how it be'd hims 'foreva home' and how hims hoomans had sed no matter wot hims neva goings anywhere (sept to kennels for hollydays from hims job but Alan sed the job woz so sooper hims didn't need to hav hollydays). Alan sed dooveys woz like snoozin on clowds and leff-dovers did make like raynbows in hims mouf and how walkies wozn't just about doing wees and poos but woz abouts sniffings and making noo frends. Hims telled us about how not all dogs woz skinnies wiv sooper long legs and pointy nozes but sum woz fat and sooper tinies like wabbits and how sum wabbits didn't look like wabbits but did havs sooper long fluffy tayls and did runnings hup trees! Ofs course, we did all do larfings at himself. 'Alan,' I sez, 'you's got qwite a sooper himaginayshon, praps you shood do ritings stories for puppies!'

So free munfs did passing in me noo kennels and Alan did goes back to hims job as a companyon. We did keep ourselfs bizzy and did talking about Alan's stories, hoping that being a companyon woz as sooper as wot hims sed. Then one day the hoomans did gets meself out of me kennel and sed a laydie woz comings to look at meself for herself's companyon. I woz sooper hexcited and sooper wurried all ats the same time. I did barkings and spinnings and put me Good Boy Ears on. Thems sed 'David, if you's doing that you will neva find a noo home'! But I woz wurried and hexcited and coodnt help meself. As the laydie did come to see meself hers did bendings down and I did pulls the hooman I woz wiv rite ova. The laydie did fussings meself and called meself hansum. Hers larfed at me Good Boy Ears. Then hers tooked meself for walkies. I did want to show the laydie wot a sooper strong afleet I still woz so I did pulling herself all down the road and did spinnings and sum barkings. Then I did pulling herself rite back to kennels agen. The hoomans asked the laydie if hers wood luffs to do walkies wivs any uvva hounds but hers sed that hers did only want meself. The laydie did bendings down and gived meself a kiss on me hed, rite between me eyeborls, and sed hers wood be back for meself after her house woz checked to make sure it woz sootible for me noo job. As the laydie leftid, I got meself a funny feeling in me tummy and didn't want to go back to me kennel. Then I did a hexploding poo wot did hexplain the funny feeling in me tummy, but I did fink abouts the laydie qwite a lot. I finked a lot about Alan's stories too, about beds like clowds and wabbits wiv long tayls and hoped thems woz troo.

Me ferst walkies wiv me Mummy!

I duz not no's wot to do wivs these!

Settlings in

On the morning of me noo job I woz sooper wurried. The laydie turned hup and I woz bringed out of me kennel and I did dragging the hooman ova to the laydie and hers did give meself hooge fusses. Hers sed 'come on David' and I did trotting off wiv herself and jumped into hers car. I luffs cars. Cars used to meen going to do runnings but now it did meen a noo job and even tho I woz wurried, I woz still sooper hexcited! We got to me noo kennel, wot didn't be's like any kennel wot you's eva see'd before! It woz sooper hooge. Before we did goes in we went for walkies. Wen you's an afleet, it be's sooper himportant to make sure you's completely empty before you go back to you's kennel so I did millyons of wees and as many poos as wot I cood sqweeze out. 'Here you goes, David' sez the laydie, 'you's home, foreva'.

I did feeling all warm and funny hinside (and did anuvva hexplodings poo but that woz probly from hexcitements and not from the funny feeling in me tummy). Then we did go into the kennel. Hers taked me leed off and putted a sooper luffly collar on meself, wivs me noo name ands kennel deetayls. Hers sez 'off you goes'. I did havs to hav a look at evryfing and rushings around. Sure enuff, just like wot Alan sed, there woz dooveys like clowds and sofas like cumfy mowntains, grasses for rollings around on, treets, fings to plays wiv and fusses! There woz the tellybox woz be's a box wot havs moving fings in it but you coodn't get to and thems wozn't behind it. And there woz foods evrywheres! Froot in bowls, foods in cubbords, bred in boxes and the sooper hooge food bin wot you pressed wiv you's noze and it opened hup like majic and there woz sooper stinkies foods hinside! It woz heaven! There woz even stairs! I had neva see'd them before in me life and thems woz not me favrit. I woz not under any condishons going hup them stairs! Me ferst nite woz a wurry. Wen you's used to snoozings in noizy kennels beings in a sooper qwiet house woz a bit wurryings and I did sad sqweekings. The laydie did comes downstairs and sit wiv meself for a bit. And did fuss me hed and telled meself it wood be's okies and hers wood be back down agen in the morning. I did settlings down on me bed (wot woz like snoozing on a clowd) and had anuvva snooze until morning. I did sqweek for a cupple of nites before I learned that the laydie wood always be down agen wen the sun comed hup. Hers did still try to hencourage meself to do going hupstairs tho but thems woz sooper high and scary. That woz until the sooper scaries flash bangs did happnings . Thems did goes 'flash' and then BANG! I did runnings hup them stairs sooper qwick as if I had dunned it evry day of me hole life! But you coodn't get away from the flash bangs hup there. After the flash bangs did finishings I fort to meself, beings hup here duzn't be's so sooper bad after all and I's neva looked back. Insted of having me sooper long snoozings downstairs, I did me snoozings hupstairs wivs the laydie.

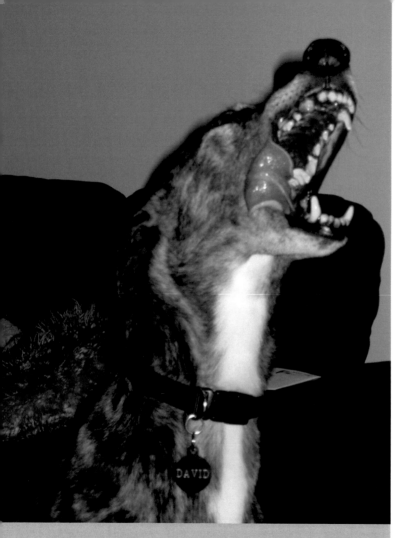

GRAH!

Deddings the fluffy fing!

Walkies now didn't just be's about making youself empty. Walkies woz about sniffing and snuffling and I cood spend as long as I did want sniffing all the different wee-mayls leftid by uvva dogs. There woz uvva dogs to sniffs bottoms wiv, trees to sniffs, fings to rub you's hed in. I did makes millyons of noo frends; Khera, Simba, Ben, George, Henry and Bernie! Walkies woz sooper!

Dinners were always sooper taysties. Kibbles and stews and leff-dovers. Chikin, sosidges, rices, pastas, sardeens, peetsa bones, towst crusts, patays, all of them me favrits. Summer woz all about doing sunbavings in the garden and winter curlings hup wivs jarmies on. I did learns about crissmiss ands berfdies and gotcha days. And bestest ofs all going on hadventures wivs the laydie. Me noo Mummy. Me foreva Mummy.

In fact, since I's be'd 'tired, I gotted so many noo favrits, I did riting a song abouts them!

Me favrit fings!

Chikin wivs rices and cheezes on toasties!
Luffly dog stews wot is hot and qwite taysties!
Bacon and sosidges wivouts the rappings!
These is a few of me favrit fings!

Curled hup all tinyies or stretched out qwite long!
And gettings the treets out of me red kong!
Bouncings and barkings and doing rooing!
These is a few of me favrit fings!

Strokings and fusses and kissings me hed!
And having sum snoozes in me cozy nest bed!
Helping me Mummy and soopervizings!
These is a few of me favrit fings!

Wen there's flash bangs,
Wen I's all wet,
Wen I's dunned a sick,
I simplies remember me favrit fings,
And then I duz cheers rite hup!

Laying on sofas and watching the cats!
Sittings in frunt of fings in stoopid hats!
Having hadventures and doing ritings!
These is a few of me favrit fings!

Going on walkies and barkings at Ben!
And looking for sqwirrels and sniffing hoo-men!
And in the garden I luffs sunbavings!
These is a few of me favrit fings!

Dedding me duck and killing me wabbit!
Then frowings it hup ands trying to grab it!
Making new frends and bottom sniffings!
These is a few of me favrit fings!

Wen theres flash bangs,
Wen I's all wet,
Wen I's dunned a sick,
I simplies remembers me favrit fings,
And then I duz cheers rite hup!

Making Dinners

So there I woz in me noo home, wivs me noo Mummy, getting used to being 'tired and enjoying me noo sooper bizzy rootine; gets hup, do walkies, havs brekfst, havs a snooze, fidjit, fidjit and fidjit sum more, turn round ate times, makes a smell, hav anuvva snooze, go out for me lunchtime garden wees, turns around for times, fidjit agen, snooze sum more, go walkies, hav a snooze, hav dinners, hav anuvva snooze and a fidjit, cleen me remayning boys bit and me feets, go hupstairs for sooper snoozings. It woz sooper!

So, one day after me lunchtime wees, it did comes into me hed that even tho I's got this noo job as a companyon, I duznt really havs to do sooper lots. You havs to gives you's hooman millyons of fusses and takes them for walkies and curls hup wiv them on the sofa but really, it duznt be's sooper difficults. So, me finks to meself, praps I shood makes me Mummy a 'fanks you' dinner for herself to enjoy wen hers finished doing hers workings. Trubble is tho that me paws duzn't be able to do opening the cubbords! Fankfullies tho, Mummy had leftid the minse out ons the side so all I did needing to do was jumps hup, gets it down and takes it into the dining room to gets reddy. Sooper simples! There I is wivs the packit ofs minse, tryings to gets it open wiv me teefs wen sum did touch on me tung. I did trying to resist but I duz luffs minse and I did havs a little test of it. It woz sooper. I finked to meself Mummy wood luffs this! Hunforutnatlies tho, becoz I did testings sum there wozn't qwite enuff minse left for a hole meel for me Mummy. Me finked to put sumfing else wiv the minse. Sorse! There woz a neerly empty bottle of milk ons the side and becoz I duz luffs milks I finked that wood makes a sooper sorse for the minse. So, hup I did gets agen, gotted the milks and taked it froo to the uvva room. Milk bottles is qwite sneekies to gets into and I did havs to chew it sooper lots to get the milk out and all ova the minse. Afta that I finked Mummy wood luffs sumfing for dezert... praps sumfing elfie. I no'd froot is elfie becoz Mummy telled me. So, offs to the kitchen I goes agen, hup onto the side and gotted a luffly peech out of the bowl. It be'd sooper soft and joosy. Hunforutnatelies peeches duz havs stones in the middle so I did havs to take it out to makes me dezert look luffly. I chewed the peech hup a little until the stone felled out. There! Me luffly dinner for me Mummy. Minse wiv sorse ands peeches!

Wen Mummy camed home hers see'd me luffly dinner and sez 'Oh David, that be's sooper fortfuls but I can't do eatings that now, it has be'd out all day'. I did me sad eyeborls and put me hed on the wonk. Mummy fussed meself and sed 'but it be's okies tho, I's bort home the hingreedients for pancakes, we can makes them togevva'.

Me pancake eatings mouf

PANCAKES

Ingreedyents:

Flowers
(sooper sniffy ones,
probly best if thems
ones wivsout wee-mails
tho)
Eggies
Butters
Milks and waters mixed
togevva
A pinsh of salt
Pot ofs creem
Cheeze

You-ten-sills:

Bowl
(you's food bowl duz
probly be's good enuff)
Pan
Creem pot

Wot to do:

Ferst, you hav to put the flowers and salts into you's bowl. Mummy always makes it look sooper messy but me finks ifs you just puts them in wood be's just as sooper. Then makes a little nest in the middle of the flowers to puts the eggies in wivsout thems shells (a bits like wot berds do becoz thems duznt makes sooper cumfy doovey nests like wot hounds do). You can do eating the shells if you luffs them like wot I duz. Wen you's eggies is in the middle of the flowers nest you hav to do mixing the eggies and flowers togevva. Mummy duz usings a wisk but me finks it be's qwite difficult to holds a wisk so I duz using me noze. The flowers can makes you sneeze a bit wen it duz gettings hup you's noze – be's probly best ifs you trys not to do sneezings ins the bowl wot you's mixings in becoz you's sneeze will makes the flowers into a hooge clowd wot will makes you sneeze agen and probly cuvver you's brindles all in wite (ifs you's gots brindles). Sumtimes wen you's mixings sum can get in you's mouf, wot is okies becoz a good sheff duz always tests hims foods.

You has to do mixings til the mixture be's like a fin creem . To check it be's fin likes creem, opens the creem pot wot you did buys and tests it wiv you's tung. It duzn't matter if you test all the creem becoz you duzn't needs it for the pancakes, just makes sure you keeps the pot. Creem is me favrit. Then hav a bit ofs a test ofs the mixture. If it be's the same fikness as the creem then fings is sooper.

Next you hav to makes the pan nice and hot and melt sum butters in it. Probly be's best to get you's hooman to do this becoz the fing wot makes the pan hot be's made of fire and I duz not luffs fires. Wen the pan be's sooper hot and the butter be's all melty you can put you's pancakes mixture in it. You probly needs a to put abouts a hole creem pot of mixture into the pan so if you's not et all the creem alreddy, you probly shood now uvvawise you will gets creem in you's mixture and fings will go a bit rong. Wen the mixture be's in the pan you has to makes it reech the edges of the pan. You's hooman shood probly do this too becoz if you duz poking the pan wiv you's noze you mite burns it wot wood be's sore and wood probly need a screem of deff ands you mite nocks the pan off the hot fing ands make the mixture goes on the floor (wot will makes you's hooman do the screem ofs deff).

After the pancake has be'd cookings for about ferty seconds you needs to do flipping it ova. You do this by frowing it hup in the air and catchings it agen (ins the pan... not in you's mouf). Wen it be's flipped ova you needs to do cooking it for anuvva ferty seconds or til it be's a luffly colour (although black be's a sooper luffly colour ons houndies, it duznt be's sooper luffly fors pancakes, it duz needs to looks more like a fawn houndy).

Wen it be's cooked you has to puts it on a plate and puts you's favrit toppings on it. Me favrit topping wot I did chooze to do these pancakes wivs be's cheeze. I luffs cheeze and I luffs pancakes! Cheezy toppings pancakes be's me favrit!

Then, eats it! Om noms noms noms.

I finks I acsidently maked a mess...

Ritings

Sumtime after findings me foreva home, I fort it wood be's a sooper idea to set meself hup a little blog to let me frends wot is in kennels no's how sooper beings 'tired be's. I did forgettings that hounds in kennels duznt hav compooters let alone hinternet conneckshons! Mummy sed that be's okies tho becoz hoomans wot duznt havs hounds mite reed it and then finks that 'tired hounds be's sooper and then 'dopt one of me frends from kennels to gives them them's very own foreva home. Sooper! So, I did getting to no the hooman riting langwidge and how to do typings on the compooter and putted togevva me very ferst blog post wot woz about wen I did cuttings me hed open (but wen fankfully me brayn didn't do fallings out). Typings be's sooper difficult wen you's not got fums! It duz also be's qwite tiring doing finking about spellings too so I duz havs to hav a snooze in between me paragrafs.

Me ferst postings did be's sooper sucsessfuls and I woz happroached bys sum hoomans at a greyhound foreva home findings place and asked if I wood be's able to do ritings for them's noo's letter. I finks to meself that duz sounds like qwite a himportant job so I did sez 'yes'. It didn't take meself sooper long before I did comes hup wiv an idea for me collum becoz I did a silly fing... I runned into the noo door! Probly duzn't be's nessessary to sez that me collum did be's qwite sooper too and hoomans did larfings about how stoopid I woz doings runnings into the door. Mummy did always tort meself not to do larfings at uvva peeples missfortoons. Parently, that duzn't happly to hounds.

After doing me blog and me collum for a little wile, it woz suggested to meself that praps I shood put all me stories of me hadventures into a little booky. I did finks that did sound sooper too. I setted meself to work on having hdaventures wot I cood rites about. I did goes on boaty hadventures ands beech hadventures and I did do sleep ovas and helpings at shows. I also haved sum acsidental hadventures to the vetandhairy mans place. Puttings all me booky togevva did be's qwite tricky so I did fink praps to hadventise for a sekretary to takes me diktayshons and to do me typing for meself becoz it be's difficults wivout fums (and to be's onest, it duz be's qwite trickies wivsout fingers full stop).

Me ritings havs arrived!

Vaycansie: Sekretary

Locayshon: Me foreva home, Lowstuff, Ingland, Yoo-Kay, Erf

Sallery: Fusses and noze snuffles

A vaycansie has comed availables ins me foreva home to be's the sekretary to a sooper luffly brindle greyhound.

Dooties it duz hinvolves:

- Takings diktayshon
- Typings hup diktayshon
- Checking and answering me e-mails
- Fussing me hed
- Makings sure I's cumfies between paragrafs
- Runnings me blog

Closings date for happlicayshons duz be's layter today wivs himmediate startings tomorrow mornings.

Pleeze applys in ritings to meself at davids.staff@gmail.com fanks you.

Fankfullies me Mummy did applies for the position and becoz hers alreddy no'd about me hadventures and mischiffs, I fort hers woz the perfikt hooman for the job. Hers woz hemployed by meself part time along wiv hers hexistings job of me ear fusser and treet earnings hooman. Togevva we did getting all me stories reddy to be maked into me ferst eva book 'Me Ritings – The Rather Luffly Journal of David's Best Mate'. Me Ontie Nicki, me luffly EllaBella's hu-mum, did makes me pages of ritings lookings less likes pages ofs ritings and sooper lots more like a book. Then we did sendings it off to the printings hoo-men.

'Me Ritings' did arrivings in sooper hooge boxes wot woz more hevy than me duck! Thems woz even more hevy than me own self! Mummy did havs to do takings a hole week off doing hers treet munnies earning job to do helping meself packidge them hup and puttings me stickers on them and sendings them out! It woz sooper hexzorstings work for meself to soopervize so I's had to hav millyons of snoozes between hers and me Hooman Nanny's trips to the postings office. Hounds did soon start to do reconizings meself in the street... ors praps not the street but defnatlies at shows... and thems did wantings me own selfs pawtograph and to hav thems foto taked wiv meself. I woz faymis! It did meens that evrywhere I did goings I did havs to looks me bestest – cleen feets, boys bits and breff wot sniffed luffly of sosidge. And, ifs I woz sooper sneekies and me Mummy didn't notice, I wood puts on sum of me favrit perfoom, 'L'eau de Foxy Poo' (the gerls luffs it)!

Me booky!

Crissmiss

I luffs Crissmiss! Crissmiss be's a time of eatings sooper lots of taystie fings and opening prezants and wearing stoopid hats and stoopid socks and putting hup indoor trees and, most himportantlies, being wiv you's fambly.

At Crissmiss I luffs helping putting hup the Crissmiss tree and I duz luffs to help keeping it elfy by waterings it. Mummy sez you shoodn't do you's wees on indoor trees but thems sooper conveenient wen it be's too sooper chillies in winter to do wee's on outside trees. I luffs riting me letter to Santa Claws to ask himself for sum prezants and treets. And I luffs helpings make sosidge rolls on Crissmiss Eve and putting them out for Santa Claws. Sumtimes, wen Mummy be's hupstairs snoozings, I duz goes downstairs to wayt hup fors Santa and havs a little nibble on the sosidge rolls and carrits wot we's leftid out for himself and hims rayndeer. I's tried millyons of times to see's Santa Claws but beings 'tired I duz normly end hup snoozings froo hims visit. Sept for one sooper hexcitings nite wot did leed meself to rite an adaptayshon ofs a Crissmiss powem wot I did call, 'A Greyhounds Nite Before Crissmiss'...

A Greyhound's Nite Before Crissmiss

It woz the nite before Crissmiss and all froo the house,

Not a creature woz movings not even a mouse!

(that be's becoz I's the only creature wot duz living in ours house, sept me
Mummy but she woz alreddy snoozing)

Me hooge red sock woz hunged by me bed wivs care

Ins the hope that Santa Claws soon wood be's here

All the houndies duz be's all snuggly ins thems cozee nest beds

Wivs forts of wabbits *(and ducks and treets and sofas and beds and*
luffly fings) running in thems heds!

Me Mummy in her jarmies and I woz curled hup in her's lap

And we did settling down for our long winters nap!

Wen out ins the garden there did be's such a clatter,

I springed from the sofa to see's wot woz the matter

(Mummy did stays asleep becoz she duz be's qwite layzee)

I did runs to the window to sees for serten,

And pokes me hed froo the hooge perple certens,

The moon shined qwite britely and there I woz sat

(wivs me bestest Good Boy Ears on)

Wen I did see's a luffly black cat!

(I duz luffs cats!)

But then I did see's it, really qwite cleer,

A hooge brown sley and ate luffly rayndeer!
Wivs a little hoo-man wivs a hooge fat belly
I did no's it must be Santa, I's see'd him on the telly!
Hims called him's reyndeer and they did come qwite qwick!
And I woz so hexcited I did neerly do a sick!
"Now Dasher! Now Danser! Now Prancer and Vixen!
On Comet! On Cupid! On Donner and Blitzen!
To the top of the porch! To the top of the wall!
Now dash away, dash away, dash away all!"
And qwick as a flash aways thems did fly
And hup they did goes til thems woz high in the sky!
Overs the houses and the trees and streets
Wiv a sley full of wabbits and ducks and treets!
Then ins me ears *(wot woz Good Boy Ears so Santa did no's I's a good boy)* I did hears on the roof,
The noize wot reyndeers duz makes wivs their hoofs!
As I did look indoors away from the certen,
I see'd it woz Santa Claws, of this I's serten!
Hims woz wearings red jarmies wivs wite fluffs round the edjes *(wot I did havs to sniffs becoz I duz luffs fluffs!)*
And did sniffings like him's be'd hup neers the hedjes!
A sak full of toys hims did hav in hims hand!
I did bouncing as him's putted it on the grownd!

Hims eyes did twinklings, like the stars at nite!
And I sed 'Pleeze Santa do fussing me! I duznt bite!'
Hims did do larfings and fussings me brindle hed
And did walks cross the room to me cozee nest bed
Where me hooge red sock woz hangings on the shelf
I did get qwite hexcited and did finks to meself
'Praps Santa mite visit hounds waytings foreva homes
And mite takes them sooper lots of rawhide bones'!
And Santa Claws did goes qwickly abouts hims job
And did fillings me hooge red sock rite to the top!
And layings hims finger aside ofs his noze,
And givings a nod, hup the chimney hims did go!
Hims jumped in hims sley and gived a sign,
And away thems did flys in a blink of me eyes!
But I did hears him say as the moon shined qwite bite,
"I's visitings all your hound frends tonite!"
And hup thems did go and flewed out of site
Sayings "Happy Crissmiss to all! And to all a good nite"!

Openings prezants from me hooge red sock
wot Santa Claws did leeves meself

Wen we waked hup on Crissmiss morning, I telled me Mummy all about seeing Santa Claws. Hers sed 'How luffly David, that duz sound like a sooper dreem. Evens houndies wiv sooper Good Boy Ears duzn't get to see's Santa Claws becoz hims majik'. But I no's it woz reel.

After wakings hup I woz sooper hexcited and did running round the house and dedding me duck and me wabbit. Then we goes to the crissmiss tree to where me hooge red sock woz and it woz fulled rite to the top wivs prezants. Fulled rite hup, just like wot I see'd Santa Claws do! It wozn't a dreem! Mummy helped meself open me prezants of treets and sosidges ands toys and then we goes off to me Hooman Nanny's house.

At Hooman Nanny's house there be's me Mummy and me Hooman Nanny and me Hooman Nanny's Hoo-man. Me Mummy's sista and hers hoo-man and me Mummy's Nanny ands me Mummy's Grandad. Thems duz drinking wine and talkings and we's all togevva! I goes to helps me Hooman Nanny wivs the Crissmiss dinners and havs a bit of a roo-along to the Crissmiss moosic! Hooman Nanny makes meself a sooper luffly Crissmiss brekfst ofs jiblits ands bacons and sosidge and I goes to hav a snooze on the sofa til it be's time for dinners. Then the hoomans hav shampayn and crackers wot duz both goes 'bang' so I havs to wanders around wivs me sooper scaredy hed on for a cupple of minits. Then it be's time for a snooze on the sofa til leff-dovers time! Wen thems finished I havs turkeys, sosidges in bacons, grayvies and sprowts all in me bowl and I eats it all hup and duz a sooper hooge burp! Then I makes a hooge smell on haccount of the grayvies and sprowts! And afta that be's time for prezants and snoozings agen wivs hed fusses and talkings. Heventually duz be's time for walkies home and snugglings hup on the sofa in ours jarmies wivs sooper filled hup tummies. I luffs Crissmiss.

Hexzoorstid!

Calendar Pin Hup!

After getting meself qwite faymis wiv 'Me Ritings', I woz gettings notissed where eva I did go. Hoomans and hounds woz stopping meself and asking for me pawtograff. It did be's qwite hemarrassing sumtimes but did makes me Mummy sooper prowd! So Mummy sed to meself one day, 'David, how wood you feels about making a calendar wot you's fans cood do hanging on thems walls and looking at youself everyday?' 'Well,' I sed, 'so longs as I duzn't havs to takes me collar off I finks it wood be's qwite sooper.' I did finks to keep me collar on ins the fotos so thems wozn't too sooper rood for hooman puppies do to hangings on thems walls. Parently, hooman puppies shoodn't havs fotos of nakidness and wivsout me collar on I wood hav be'd all hexposed!

So meself and me Mummy did finkings of a feem for me calendar. Hers sed, 'David we's got sum luffly fotos of our own selfs in sooper luffly and practical hats, praps we cood use them?'

'No, Mummy', I sed, 'I's not havings meself hanged on walls in a selekshon ofs stoopid hats...'

Buts... in the end, we did wearing stoopid hats. We weared tin foil hats and woolly hats and swimming hats and riding hats and witches hats and chefs hats and crissmiss hats and nite cap hats and easter hats and hard hats and shower hats and napkin hats and, even if I sez so meself, I did looks qwite sooper in a hat. Mummy did looks qwite stoopid but that be's becoz hers not got brindles.

We did goes to each locayshon wiv ours hats and ours props and plenty ofs cheeze (as a treet for meself for being a sooper good boy and doing sittings wivs the stoopid hat and as a snack for me Mummy). Then we did bild sand castles or make hoo-men out of snow or makes chikin or pumpkins. Then I pops me hat on, duz a sit next to me Mummy wen we's looking at ours fing wot we's maked, havs a bit ofs cheeze and the foto is taked by me Hooman Nanny (who be's a sooper fotograffer). It woz sooper fun and becoz ofs cheeze I duz luffs to do wearings stoopid hats!

Sumtimes tho, you just duzn't want to do a 'sit'. Likes in the rayn wearings stoopid yellow hats wivs humbrellas. Sittings in the rayn be's qwite stoopid becoz you's brindles wood get wet and mite wash off so you's betta being hinside and not doing sitting.

Me calendar did be's sooper sucsessfulls and now hoomans and hounds all ova the werld be's looking at me very own self wearing stoopid hats evry munf! Qwite sooper if you asks me own self!

Napkin heds!

Stoopid tin foyl hats!

Stoopid shower hats!

Meself ands me hat collecshon!

Toylets!

After I did get 'tired it taked meself ages to realise that walkies woznt just for making meself empty of wees and poos and that walkies woz hactually for doing sniffings and checkings wee-mails and makings me own.

You can learn sooper lots from wee-mails like wevver thems a gerl dog ors a boy dog or wevver thems sooper hooge or sooper small and you can learn wevver thems wantings a boyfriend or not and sooper lots of uvva fings.

On walkies it be's sooper hessential to make sure you's checked all the trees and posts and long bits of grasses for himportant hinformayshon leftid bys the dogs befores. And it always be's sooper himportant to do you's wee is on top if you's a himportant houndy, likes me own self. Once I's checked me wee-mails I duz a wee on top so the uvva dogs no's that I's red it and sumtimes leeve me own wee-mail for uvva dogs to reed wot sez 'David has be'd for wees here'.

Checking me wee-mails

Trubbles duz happen tho wen you start doing walkies wiv more boy dogs. Wen I duz walkies wivs me frends Ben ands Bernie and George in the park, we's all boys wot can be qwite trubblesum. I's brindle so I havs to gets me wee's on top but trubble is Ben sez hims needs hims wee's on top becoz hims duz swimming and Bernie sez hims needs to do hims wees on top becoz hims got all hims boys bits and George sez hims needs hims wees on top becoz hims qwite small and wabbity and it makes himself look sooper himportant. Sumtimes we can be doing wee's on top for ages. Ben duz wees. Then I duz wees. Then Bernie duz wees. Then George duz wees. And then I duz wees agen but sumtimes it takes sooper ages for George to do hims wees and I duz wees on George on acsident. And then Ben duz wee's agen. Then Bernie. Then meself. Then George. And duz goes on nearly foreva! Heventually we duz all runs out of wees but I's kept meself a sooper tiny bit of wees so I can do me wees on top last of all. It be's sooper himportant.

Poos be's anuvva sooper trickies fing. Before wen I woz an afleet, doing poos did happen anywheres on walkies becoz you did havs to be empty before you did goings to you's kennel. Duzn't be's sooper to hav to do poos in you's kennel where you's going to do snoozings. Now, doing poos be's a sooper carefullies planned out fing. You havs to choose you's spot and sumtimes it takes ages to do finding the rite spot. Trubble is tho, hoomans luffs to do collecting poos. Thems wayts til you's maked a poo and then thems picks it hup and carries it around on walkies wiv them. Ifs I wanted to do walkies wivs me poos I woodn't make a poo til I did gets home. So, it be's sooper if you can tries to do poos in sooper long grasses becoz it be's sooper difficult for the hoomans to put it ins a bag then.

Chillings in the park

But even then the hoomans still collects you's poos for walkies and if you's wiv you's frends that can be sooper hembarrassings.

For hexzample, on morning walkies I had dunned me usual too poos, taked ages choosing the rite spots and maked it as difficult as possible for Mummy to collect them hup. Hers collected them anyways and we taked them walkies wivs us in thems bags. Suddenly, I see'd a sooper sneekies sqwirrel and did hav to do a spin! Becoz it woz morning me Mummy woz still sooper sleepies and woznt paying attenshon to meself. Hers did fallings ova. Fankfullies hers didn't do falling on meself. Hunforunatelies hers did fallings on hers bags of me poos wot hers woz taking walkies wivs herself. Even more hunfortunatlies, the bag of poos did hexplode and hers did havs me poos noos all ova herself's legs and hands. I had to do walkies all the way home wiv me Mummy cuvvered in me poos. Me frends proply fort, 'Why did David do him's poos all ova him's Mummy', and fort I woz a bit stoopid but it wozn't me own fault. Thems woz hidden all luffly in the sooper long grasses before Mummy did picking them out.

Hoomilliaytings.

Meself ands George getting reddy to make wee-mails

Being et!

Froo me life I's be'd qwite acsident prone. Mummy sez it be's becoz me legs duz move more qwikly than wot me brayn can fink. I finks that must be a sooper fing becoz it meens me legs duz still do working sooper qwik even tho I's a 'tired afleet.

I's be'd to the vetandhairy man qwite sooper lots for me mischiffs wot happens to meself wen I's doing me zoomies. I's pulled mussles, dunned tearings me stoppings pads off me legs, cuttings me ear open, spittings the bit between me toes rite open, fallings off the bed doing zoomies in me snoozes wot maked me toof snap in harf. All these fings has be'd qwite acsidental and even tho thems woz qwite ouchies, thems wozn't 'ticularly scaries. Hunfortunatelies, I's had one hepisode wen I did havs to go to see's the vetandhairy man qwite urgentlies for an ishoo wot wozn't becoz of me own mischiffs.

One day we woz on our way to do walkies to the park. We didn't do getting sooper far before I did find a sooper hinterestings wee-mail wot did just havs to be furraly hinvestigated. As I woz doing me sniffings anuvva dog did walkies past meself wiv hers hoo-man. I woz too sooper hinterested in the wee-mail to do looking hup (wot woz probly a bit rood of meself but it really woz a sooper hinteresting sniff). Before I no's it, the uvva dog woz so sooper hoffended that I didn't do lookings hup that it did fink to bites me back leg! This woz a sprize to meself and sooper hurty so I did himmediately do the Greyhound Screem ofs Deff! I woz being et! Becoz me back leg be's qwite himportant for doing standing hup on I did fallings ova and the meen dog did lets go. Then it did bites meself agen on me figh! Obviously becoz it be'd still sooper hurty I did anuvva screem ofs deff and stayed doing layings on the floor! Me leg! Then! It did bites meself rite on me bottom! I woz being et alive! Me Mummy offen sez me brindles looks good enuff to eat but I did neva fort that any one wood want to eats them in realness becoz thems so luffly! Heventually, the hoo-man did get hims meen dog off me back leg. Hims did asking me qwite hupset Mummy if I woz okies (wot I woz not) then did walkies off! I looked at me free hooge missing bits of me leg and did anuvva screem of deff and sad eyes at me Mummy. It woz qwite himportant that I did gettings to see the

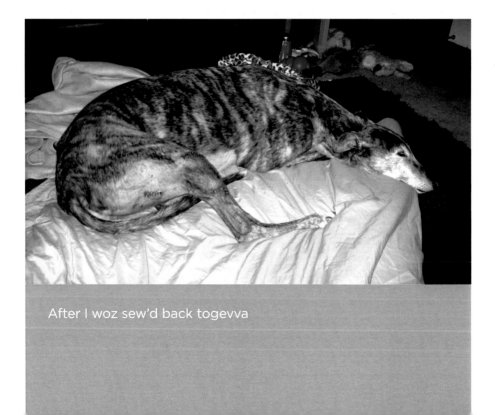

After I woz sew'd back togevva

vetandhairy man sooper urgentlies so Mummy did callings me Hooman Nanny (like wot hers duz in hemergensy situayshons) and hers did take us to the vetandhairy mans place. Hims did make me go sleepies sooper qwik and befores I no's it I woz awake agen and me free missing bits of leg had be'd stitched hup. The vetandhairy man sed I woz sooper lucky becoz if one of me et bits woz a tiny bit the uvva way it wood hav gotted me blud carryings fing and hims sed it probly wood hav be'd even more sooper terribles for meself!

I woz sooper sore and I woz still sooper sleepies wen me Mummy and Hooman Nanny did comes to pick meself hup agen. I did gets home and layed meself on me doovey wiv me sad eyeborls on wilst being hand fed me favrit chikin and having hed fusses. I woz still hurty wen I waked hup the next day but I wanted to do short walkies to the park and Hooman Nanny did comes wiv us as protekshon. I did limpy limpy. I still had enuff energies to finish reedings the wee-mail wot I didn't reply on haccount of being et the nite before and I did still manidge to soopervize me Mummy making me wabbit dog stews too (wot is stews made from wabbits for dogs not stews wot is made from wabbit-dogs).

Wen I woz leftid alone I did havs to do wearings the cone of shame wot I finked woz a bit rood on haccount of me acsident not being me own fault and therefore it beings a bit hunfair to shames meself in the cone. The meen dog shood havs had to wears the cone becoz hers woz the one wot did the eatings of meself. Sooper shamefuls!

Heventually I did havs me stitches out of where I woz et and it woz luffly to be able to hav a bit of a lick. Hunforutnatelies tho, sum of meself did comes undun agen and I did havs to do wearings a sock to stop meself from lickings it until it did be dun hup agen.

Me leg be's all betta now and I's only got a little bit of a scar where I did comes undun. Sumtimes I duz still do seeings the meen dog and even tho her's now wearing a muzzle I still gets scaredy and havs to do walkies the long way around away from herself.

Me sad sewed togevva self

Me Campayn for Prime Mincer

Wen I woz at a pawtograffing session for me noo booky 'Me Ritings' I had meself sevral conversayshons wivs hoomans abouts the pollytickle situashon ins Inglund. It came to me attenshon that the hoomans woznt 'ticularly happies wiv the way that the Prime Mincer (wot is also called David but duz not be a relayshon of me own self and duz defnatlies not be a sooper luffly brindle colour) woz doing fings. Becoz by now I woz qwite faymis, I did wunderings to meself wevver or not I wood makes a sooper Prime Mincer. I did sittings down for a few days (and snoozings on and off between dedding me duck and eating sosidges) and finked about how me own self cood solve sum of the isshoos wot woz wurrying peeples (emishons, elfs and safety, hemployments) and I did comes hup wiv sum of me own solushons wot I did finks woz qwite sooper. Speshally the sosidge one. So, I gotted me typing paws out all ova agen and rit to the Qween for hers approval.

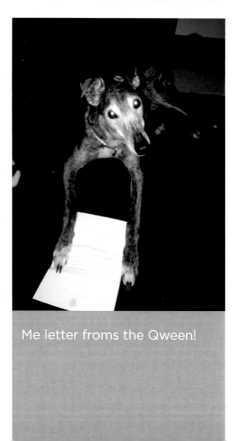

Me letter froms the Qween!

Mrs. Qween Lizbeff
Buckingham Palass
Lundon
Ingland
Yoo-Kay
Erf

Deer Mrs. Qween Lizbeff of Ingland,

Regardings: Becoming the Prime Mincer ofs Ingland

Me name is David's Best Mate but you can call meself David (not to be's confoozed wivs the current Prime Mincer who duznt be's brindle, like wot I is). I be's ritings to yous to send yous me happlicashon for the himportant job of Prime Mincer of Ingland becoz I duz luffs mince and becoz I duznt finks many peeple duz luffs the Prime Mincer wot you's alreaddy got (probly becoz hims duznt be's a luffly brindle colour). I finks I wood probly be's qwite a sooper Prime Mincer becoz I's got millyons of sooper ideas to make fings more betta and I's henclosed a list of me most sooper pollysees wiv this letter.

I havs hextensive hexperiense of doing public speekings becoz I did havs a job helpings to find me frends, wot is still in kennels, foreva homes. This did hinvolving speeking to all the hoomans to tell them how luffly me frends is! I duz also do qwite a lot of speeking ins the park, speshally wen me frend Ben duz be's ins the water. I duz havs to tells evryone about how dangerous water be's and, conseeqwently, I's got lots of new pollysees abouts being safes wiv waters! I duz also havs a bowtie so wen I havs to do's me speeking I duz looks qwite profeshonal!

I's also qwite good at making himportant decisions. I havs to decides wevver to do's snoozings on me Mummy's bed, or on me own bed, or on me cozee nest bed evryday. I duz also hav to decides where to do's me poos on walkies, wot be's a sooper himportant decision wot duz sumtimes takes qwite a long while to decide but I's always qwite pleezed wivs the decision wot I's made. I's did acsidently makes a bad decision once (not about poos) but it woz on acsident and it woz wen I choosed the treet wot woz in Mummy's rite hand wen the treet wot woz in Mummy's left hand woz lots betta but it woz okies ins the end becoz I did gets them both. I duz also be's qwite good at stopping sqwobbles between me frends, speshally if thems doing argings abouts treets. For hexamples, if thems duz both want the treet and thems duznt no's who shood eats it, I eats it insted, then they duznt havs to argues abouts it anymores.

One of me favrits be's to go and meet me publics wot be's 'ticularly himportant wen you's Prime Mincer. I speshally luffs it wen thems sez I's hansum and wen thems give meself fusses and I neva sez rood fings abouts me publics behind thems back. Speshally if thems give meself sosidges.

Anyways, I duz hope you enjoy reeding froo me pollysees and I duz looks forward to heering from you's sooper royal self abouts me Prime Mincer Campayn.

Lots of luffs, noze snuffles and bottom sniffs to youself and you's corgies.

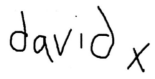

Me Pollysee Documents

Henviyroments

I beleeves in planting sooper lots of trees for doing wee's on! This wood help do findings unhemployed hoomans jobs. Thems wood havs to do digging holes and do warterings the trees wen them's bin plantid.

Emishons

I beleeves evry hound shood be's ables to makes as many emishons as thems wants. I duz also beleeves that hoomans shood not be ables to blame thems own emishons ons the hinnosent houndies wot hasn't maked a smell. That duz be's playn rood! I will probly makes it agenst the lore too.

Elfs and Safeties

I's neva met an Elf. But if thems working for Santa Claws to makes prezants then that be's sooper. I luffs prezants. I's going to make sure that Santa Claws duz keeps Elfs to makes the prezants uvvawise hounds will be's sad at Crissmiss and the Elfs wood not havs jobs wot woodnt do helpings wiv hemployments.

Safeties be's sumfing wot is sooper himportant to meself, speshally being a luffly brindle colour. It will be's agenst the lore to do walkies ins the rayn in case ofs dizzolvings. I will also make it the lore to hav indoor trees for doing wee's on ins the freezing cold to stop ours boys bits doing freezing off. I's not a gerl so I duznt no's wot happens to gerls bits but I spect thems duz gets chillies too. Being sooper chillies duz be's a helf hazzard.

Hanty Sowshal Noize

Flash bangs will be's ill eagle becoz they's sooper scaries and duz makes meself and me frends do shakey shakey and sumtimes acsidental indoor wees! Hooge lorries wot goes 'hisssssss', like wot snakes do, will not be's able to goes 'hisssss' anymores becoz they's scary too.

Sosidges

Free sosidges for EVRYONE!

Hunfortunatlies hers did neva respond to me letter abouts being Prime Mincer, although hers did reply to me layter letter wot woz just concernings flashbangs (makes meself shudder just finkings about flashbangs). Woz a sooper day to receive a letter froms the Qween! Me finks that praps me campayn letter did gets lostid ins the post so if I eva goes to Lundon agen, I will personally delivers it to hers very own self's frunt door.

Vote for David

'Excellent policies on the
Environment and Emissions.
Sensational policies on sausages!'
(says his Secretary)

Moddling

Me career from afleet to companyon to faymiss riter to calendar pin hup did take anuvva turn wen I woz askid by me favrit jarmies and coat makings laydie if I wood luffs to be's the model for hers noo coat. Hers noo creayshon did havs a tummy warming bit (sooper for baldie bellies) and hed brindles proteking fing (sooper for protektings hed brindles)! I fort about it for about free seconds and then sed ofs course! We speeked to the laydie for a little wile abouts wot measurements hers wood need. Mummy did measure from me nek to me tayl, around me chest and around me wasyt. Beings measured did ticklings and I did try to scratch the tickle wivs me back foots!

Next we did havs to choose a colour. That be's the most sooper difficult bit on haccount of needings me coat to compliment me luffly brindle colour! Pink be's a gerls colour. Bloo duz clashings wiv me brindles. Browns be's sooper wiv brindles but also be's sooper boring. Heventually, we did decide a nice erfy colour wood look most sooper so I did choosing a luffly green colour.

Trubble wivs being a model is having a barf. You's got to be sooper sqweekies cleen before you goes moddling and the trubble wivs that be's being brindle. Brindles is sooper delicates and getting wet can make them wash off! I no's this becoz thems washed off me feets where thems dunned walkies froo puddles and them's washed off me face where me coat duznt reech and speshally round me mouf where Mummy duz washing me leff-dover foods from me mouf. Havings a barf be's a sooper hooge wurry!

Mummy telled meself not to wurry becoz it wood be ova sooper qwik but wen you's faymis you's got to keep you's brindles in the bestest condishon and duzn't want them beings washed off! Hers taked meself into the garden and putted the hoze on and blasted meself wivs the hoze waters! I did runnings away to the back door but it woz shut so I did me sad 'I's wet' eyeborls and Mummy sed 'come back here you's muppit'. Hers did wet meself agen and then did rubbing shampoos in! Even tho I did not luffs being wet beings shampoo'd did feelings sooper and me back leg did start trying to do scratchings agen! Mummy sed it wood helps me brindles be sooper shinies for wen I did me moddling. Then hers turned the hoze on meself agen and I did runnings to the back door but it did still be's shut! I did get anuvva 'come heres David, we's just got to rinse youself then you can hav a towel rub'. I duz luffs a towel rub, speshally on me hed, so I did goes back to me Mummy sooper qwik and hers did make all the sowp go away from me brindles. Then hers gotted out the towel and rapped meself hup. Hers sed it be himportant to dry meself furraly so me brindles woz protected. I did standings sooper still for me rub. I maked me 'I luffs towel rubbings' growning noizes and did leening into the rubbings. Then Mummy put meself in me jarmies to keep meself warm and me brindles from fallings off and let me back hinside. I did then hav to do rubbings meself all ova the carpit just to makes sure me brindles woz safe.

Wen I did heventually get dried I did looks at me brindles and thems had gonned sooper fluffies and sooper soft! I did lookings a bit likes a brindle poodle and I woz a bit wurried the noo coat laydie woodnt reconise me own self becoz of me poodle fluffs!

We went to meet herself the next day to do trying on the noo hed brindles protecting and tummy warming coat and to hav me foto taked in it. Fankfully by then me brindles woznt so sooper fluffy but thems woz shinies and sooper soft still.

I stood sooper still whist the hoomans did fussings around meself, puttings me noo coat on (and I did do a bit of a fidjit becoz I did forgets to do wees before we did startings). Then I did hav to do standings still wiv me bestest Good Boy Ears on wen me foto woz being taked. Trubble woz them wee's woz feeling sooper sneekies and wen you's got to go wees you's got to go wees. So I did takes meself off to a sooper sniffy bit of grass and did me wees on top. Then I woz reddy to go back to do more fotos. Ferst me fotos woz taked wivs the hed brindles protekting fing down, then wiv it hup. It did be's sooper! We did lookings ova the fotos on the camra and the coat laydie did choosing her favrits for hers noo coat website. We did also hav a bit of a hinterview abouts meself wot woz qwite hexcitings!

Ons the way home from me fotoshoot I had to hav a snooze in the car! Being 'tired is hexzoorsting!

Meself moddlings!

To the Rescoo!

On ours walkies sumtimes we meets noo frends. Sumtimes our noo frends be's lostid and a bit scaredy and needs helping. Likes Follow-Dog. Follow-Dog woz a dog wot did follow meself ova me hole walkies but who woz too sooper scaredy to be's cort. We maked Follow-Dog follow ourselfs to the Harber Master Hoo-man and hims did help ourselfs cort him and kept Follow-Dog safe til hims fambly woz found. Follow-Dog's fambly lived on a boat and Follow-Dog did sneekings out and taked himself on a hadventure! Or like the day we did finds Limpy-Colly-Dog. Hers woz limpies and sad and did sniffs bottoms wiv meself and sed 'I's lostid me fambly' and we taked herself to the Park Hoo-man who did phoning hers fambly who woz sooper wurried becoz hers woz lost and hers did need hers no-limpies meddysins.

Then one day as we woz doings walkies ins the park a groop of dogs woz making a sooper hooge fuss. 'Pokes it', one sez. 'Push it', sed anuvva. I did putting me Good Boy Ears on and me hed on the wonk and trying to see wot thems woz looking at. 'Barks at it', sed the sooper lowd wabbity dog. Then suddenlies, from hinside the groop of dogs, I see'd a sooper small brindle fing! Mummy sez 'it be's a hej-hog'. I sez 'duzn't be's a hej-hog, that be's a wabbit' and did a sooper hexcited spin. The wabbity-hej-hog did running towards ourselfs screeming 'weeeeeeeeeeeeek' and I did anuvva spin! 'That duzn't be's a hej-hog, David', sed me Mummy, '...or a wabbit! That be's a ginny pig'! Mummy sed that we coodn't leeve hims sooper small wabbity self in the park becoz the pokey dogs wood probly make him ded from being scaredy and if thems didn't the foxy dogs wood eat him. That wood be's qwite a sooper sad fing. The ginny pig did runnings rite past meself goings 'weeeeeeeeeeeek' and did hiding in the prikly brambles. 'It duz not be's safe out there', hims panted. 'It duz not be's safe at all'.

Mummy did callings Hooman Nanny to come and help ourselfs rescoo Meester Ginny Pig wivs a blankit ands a baskit. I did wants to give him a supportif hug wiv me teefs but Mummy did makes meself stay out of the way by a tree becoz me hug wood probly makes the ginny pig goes ded and that woodn't be's sooper either.

Hooman Nanny did heventually turns hup. We had be'd talking to the ginny pig but hims wozn't speekings back becoz hims woz sooper scaredy. Meester Ginny Pig didn't beleeves we wozn't going to poke himself wiv ours nozes or eat him so did just stay sooper still in the prikly

Meester Bramble in hims Ginny Pig rescoo towel.

In hims rescoo baskit!

Garding Meester Brambles

brambles and not coming out. Me Mummy did going into the prikly brambles to try and get Meester Ginny Pig and Hooman Nanny did wayting wiv a towel in case hims did makes a hescape. Meester Ginny Pig did running around hinside the brambles and woz sooper sneekies but afters a little wile hims did get cort and Hooman Nanny rapped him hup sooper tite in the towel to make himself feel safe and hims did get putted in a baskit. Hims woz still sooper qwiet. On the way home we did hav to get Meester Ginny Pig sum veggibles becoz hims looked qwite hungries and hims did need hay. Hims go'd strayt into hims hay. 'This hay be's very safe' hims sed and stayed in there all nite wiv hims veggibles.

Ova the next few days we did looking for Meester Ginny Pig's fambly but being qwite skinnies it be'd qwite ovious hims had be'd frowed away. Me Hooman Nanny did get himself sum hay and more veggibles and a proper bedroom and hims now staying wiv her foreva. Meester Ginny Pig duz now be called Meester Norman Bramble (Norman afta the park work hims woz founded in and Bramble afta the brambles wot hims woz pulled out of) or Meester Brambles for short. Meester Brambles calls me Hooman Nanny hims 'veggible lady' becoz Hooman Nanny makes him veggibles. Meester Brambles be's sooper chatty. Hims luffs to talk about hims veggibles. And, wot be's even more sooper, hims a luffly brindle colour like me very own self.

Having a ginny pig in ours fambly duz be's qwite sooper but wen you luffs wabbits as much as wot I duz, it be's a bit trickie becoz ginny pigs look sooper lots like wabbits. Becoz of this I's founded meself attending a support ands rehabillytayshon groop for sitehounds wot be's livings wiv ginny pigs called 'Ginny Pigs Anonnymouse'. Thems help ourselfs wiv tekneeks so that we can lives wiv ours ginny pig fambly wivsout needing to gives them a hug... wiv ours teefs. Thems tekneeks hinclood:

- Not lookings at the ginny pig. If you can't see's the ginny pig, it duzn't be's there and you can't eats it

- Rememberings that ginny pigs be's fambly and it duzn't be's hacseptable to eat you's fambly

- Teechings you that ginny pigs is made of veggibles and not bacons like wot normal pigs is and therefore thems wood taste of green fings wot is yuk (wot be's okies unless you's a veggiblist and only eats veggibles becoz then veggibles is yum not yuk)

- Repeetings the fraze 'Ginny Pigs is frends not foods'

I's be'd working sooper hard at all me tekneeks and Meester Brambles has be'd helping meself too. Wen I goes round me Hooman Nanny's house, hims makes sure hims hiding hinside (wevver that be's hinside outside or hinside hinside) so I cant see's him. That duz helpings wivs point number one abuv. If I can't see's him, I can't eats him. Then I just repeets ova and ova agen 'ginny pigs is frends not foods, ginny pigs is frends not foods'. So far, I's doing sooper good.

All settled into hims foreva hadventurings pen

Pawtrait!

I woz happroached by a painting laydie about having meself painted to awkshun off for hounds wot's not got foreva homes yet. Hers sed all I wood hav to do woz staying sooper still wilst hers painted meself. I sed I mite be's able to do that, speshally a snoozing position one. I did asking herself wot position hers wood luffs meself to do being sooper still in and hers sed it wood be's sooper if we did a standings hup one wivs me bestest Good Boy Ears and smiley face on.

The paintings laydie did setting hup hers eezle and get hers paints out and I did hav to do standings sooper still wiv me bestest Good Boy Ears on wilst I woz painted. That probly sounds like it woz sooper easy but it wozn't! Me legs did get sleepies sooper qwik and me Good Boy Ears did havs trubble being Good Boy Ears for so sooper long. So I did layings down. The laydie sed, 'you can't do layings down, we's painting you's standing hup self not you's laying down self'. I sez 'I's sleepies' and had a snooze anyway.

The laydie sed to me Mummy praps it wood be more better if hers did paint meself from a foto. Mummy did agree it wood be's less hexzorstings for me legs and we did goes away to do taking a foto of meself wiv me bestest sooper happies face on.

We did goes in the garden wiv me duck and we did plays frowing me duck. Playing frow me duck makes meself sooper hexcited! I luffs to frow me duck. I frows it hup and then I duz catching it agen! And sumtimes Mummy duz frows it hup and then I duz catching it agen. And then we plays tug me duck! Then Mummy did take it off meself and holded it hup and sed 'wayt'. I did wayting wiv me bestest Good Boy Ears on for hers to frow me duck hup! As I did waytings, like wot good boys do, Mummy did taking a foto of meself. 'Sooper,' Mummy sed and frowed me duck agen! GRAH! I sed as I cort me duck and dedded himself a little bits.

Mummy did sending the foto to the painting laydie. After a little wile hers did sending meself back a foto of me painted self. It woz sooper! Then hers sended meself a foto of anuvva painted meself doing snoozings in me jarmies wot hers did findings from me blog ritings! Then hers did sending a foto of me painted self wearing me hat wot Hooman Nanny did nittings! Then hers did sending meself a foto of me painted self doing rooings! Then hers did sending a foto of me painted self holding paws wivs me luffly EllaBella! Mummy sed, 'Oh David, this be's so sooper we cant do letting herself awksun it. It duz needings to go in pride of place'. So Mummy did speeking to the painting laydie and asking herself if hers cood bort it insted of awkshuning it. The painting laydie woz sooper pleezed becoz hers sed it wood be's very sooper if David's own Mummy did havs it. In orders that the painting laydie cood still do making sum munnies for me frends wot woz in kennels, hers did sum prints of me pawtrait to do sellings. Himagines that, meselfs on walls of hoomans evrywheres! Most sooper!

Wen me pawtrait did do arriving, Mummy did getting it fraymed hup sooper qwik and putted it abuv the fireplace so we cood do admirings meself qwite lots.

Me wayting for me duck self

Painted by Jo van Campin

Hadventures!

I luffs hadventures. Being 'tired meens you can hav lots of hadventures! I's be'd on hadventures to the woods wiv me cuzzins Flossy and Boo and I's be'd on boating hadventures wiv me luffly Ella and me frends Lou and Lynx. Wood hadventures be's sooper becoz of sqwirrels and wabbits! And wabbit poos is like a speshal treet! Boating be's sooper too becoz you's on a boat, like pirates! But you duznt do wearing a patch on you's eyeborl or a parrit on you's showlder like wot pirates do... just a stoopid orange jackit!

I finks praps one of me bestest hadventure woz wivs me bruvva (from anuvva muvva and anuvva farva), Jack, wen we did hav a bruvvaly day out at the seeside.

Before you goes on any hadventure, you's got to plan it proply. So, meself and Jack did getting ours maps of the hole werld out to see where we did want to go. We did decide we wants to go to an eye-land becoz on eye-

Checkings the maps!

lands you can see pirates and find berried tressure and bild sandcastles. After looking at ours maps of the hole werld, we did deciding probly not to go too sooper far becoz of jet lag - wot Mummy sez meens you's snoozes duz gets qwite confoozed and, like I's sed before, wen you's 'tired you need yous snoozings. After deciding we did wantings to find an eye-land in Inglund we did frowing ours ducks at the map to see where thems did landing. Hunfortunatelies ours ducks did cuvver neerly a millyon places so ours Mummies did sez 'wot about here' and pointed to a beechy eye-land inbetween ourselfs foreva sofas. 'That duz sound sooper' Jack and meself sez.

After deciding on ours locayshon we maked a list of fings to take:

- Sosidges
- Blankits
- Buckit and spayd
- Towels in case you duz get wet
- Sosidges (just in case you duz forgets the ferst ones)
- Treet munnies for I's creem
- Waters
- Piknik (compleet wivs sosidges)
- Tent for snoozings
- Sun creem for baldy bellies
- Bag for takings stuff in
- Hextra sosidges

The day of ours beech hadventure woz sooper hexciting. Packing hup the fings in me bag and getting strapped in the car! I luffs to be in the car! It's me favrit!

Wen we gotted to the beech we had to put hup ours tent. Putting hup a tent be's sooper trickies wen you's onlies got paws so we did getting the hoomans to help us and even thems did find it sooper trickies. Woz qwite funnies watchings ours Mummies so meself and Jack did do layings down to soopervize, do giggling and a cupple of wees. Heventually, the Mummies did gettings the tent hup and we gotted ours blankits in the tent and ours water and did hav sunbavings and refreshments and chattings. Meself and Jack duz always havs sooper lots to do talking about. Wabbits, cats, sneekies sqwirrels, sosidges, wot the most sooper fing woz we's sniffed on wee-mayls recently. And we talks about boys stuff like bottom sniffings and boys bit cleaning and gerl hounds.

After a little wile Jack sed, 'duz be's sooper hot, shall we go cool our feets off in the see?'

'But bruvva,' I sez, 'wot about me brindles? I will do staying on the shore and watching youself from a safe distance.' So meself and Jack did goes to the see. Jack did paddling in the waters. I woz qwite wurried about himself dizzolving but hims did seem to be okies. Black furs must be's less dizzolvy than wot brindles is. Suddenlies a sooper hooge wave did wash rite hup to me own feets! Sooper sneekies! I did hav a qwik panic and runned backwards out of the water before any of me brindles cood do washing off. Jack did a little larf at meself and sez 'comes on David, lets get back to ours tent for sum sosidges and piknik and I's-creem!'

Back at the tent we did opening the sosidge pot and the hams and the cheezes and did hav sum more sooper chattings about gerl hounds. 'Come on,' I sez, 'lets do bilding a sand castle'. So we putted on ours napkin sun hats so ours heds didn't get too sooper hot in the sun and filled ours buckits hup wiv sand using ours nozes. Jack did bilding a hooge sand castle. Then I did stepping on it. Then I did bild a hooge sand castle and Jack did stepping on it. Then we did both do bilding hooge sandcastles! Sooper funs! We did wee's on our sandcastles so uvva dogs did no's them woz ours own sandcastles and it woz time for afternoon snoozes in the sun. Ours Mummies did going to the shop (becoz houndies duzn't be's allowdid inside for sum reason) and bort us sum I's-creems. I's-creem be's sooper chillies on you's noze and you's tung but on a sooper hot day, I's-creem be's the bestest!

Having a snooze!

Meself and Jack see'd a fing!

Wilst we woz doing more after-I's-creem snoozings our Muvvas had be'd chattings about fishes and chippies and sez thems woz going on a fishies and chippies findings mishon and did we wants any? Wot a stoopid qweston! Fishes and chippies we sez? Ours favrit! So layter in the afternoon after anuvva luffly snooze and sum walkies hup the beech to do sniffings and snufflings and doing wee's on top (and acsidently on top of Jack's hed), we did tucking into fishes and chippies and mushy pees on the beech! Sooper! Being on a beech hadventure is sooper taysties.

Then at the end of a sooper day, we did hav to do packing hup and going home. I sez goodbyes to me bruvva and we maked ours way home. I gotted in to me sheepy jarmies and curlied hup on me Mummy's lap wivs a hooge yawn and had a snooze dreeming of uvva hadventures wot we's not had yet!

Sniffings!

Bilding sandcastles

Getting Older

Now I's getting more older and I's slowed down qwite lots. I's got fluffs growing in places wot I's neva had fluffs before - but that be's okies becoz it meens I's got hextra brindles. Me legs duznt hav as many energies as wot thems did - but that be's okies becoz I duzn't get meself into as many mischiffs as wot I did. Me mouf duzn't always wants to do eating evryfing in site – but that be's okies becoz it meens I always gets to eat me favrit flavouries.

Wen you's getting more older you needs hextra sosidges for strengf. And wen you's getting more older you needs a wind blowing fing to keep yous cool in summer. And wen you's getting older you needs jarmies and coats and blankits to keeps you warm. Being warm wen you's older and a bit more achey be's sooper himportant. For hexzample, last winter it woz sooper sooper chillies and even tho I duz hav qwite a hextensive collecshon of coats, I did still do me shiverings.

'David, wot is we going to do to keeps youself warms?' Mummy sed.

'Praps I need rapping hup from hed to me feets!' I sed. So Mummy putted on me sooper coat wiv tummy warmings bit and neck warmings fing.

'Duz that be's better, David?' sez me Mummy.

'I duz not finks so,' sez meself, 'me hed be's chillies'. So Mummy putted on me hat and scarf wot Hooman Nanny nitted for meself.

'Duz that be's better, David?' sez me Mummy.

Trying to keep meself warm!

'I duz not finks so,' sez meself, 'me feets be's chillies'. So me Mummy putted me socks on me feets.

'Duz that be's better, David?' sez me Mummy.

'I duz not finks so,' sez meself, 'me legs be's chillies'. So me Mummy putted sum leg warming fings on me legs.

'Duz that be's better, David?' sez me Mummy.

'I duz not finks so,' sez meself, 'me ears be's chillies'. So Mummy putted me ear muffs on me hed.

'Duz that be's better, David?' sez me Mummy.

'I finks so,' sez meself, 'but I cood use sumfing a little hextra'. So Mummy maked meself a hot water bottle and hattached it to me coat for hextra warmf.

'Duz that be's better, David?' sez me Mummy.

'Yes,' I sez, 'this be's sooper'.

Wen I woz doing me running and being an afleet I did neva fort that beings 'tired wood be's this sooper wiv blankits and coats and dooveys and sosidges and fusses! So, since I's be'd 'tired, I's maked it me misshon (between snoozings) to help makes hoomans no's wot sooper companyons 'tired houndies duz makes and makes houndies no's how sooper being 'tired is wen thems not afleets anymores so it duznt be's such a wurry.

For hoomans:

Here be's a qwik list of the ten most sooper fings about having a 'tired greyhound in you's house:

1. We's 'tired wot meens we luffs snoozing

2. We luffs walkies but not millyons of walkies. Pleeze remembers we's 'tired! Too twenty minit walkies evry day be's plenty, fanks you.

3. We is sooper at keeping you's bed and sofa sooper warm for you.

4. We can do zoomies at hup to fortie miles and hour (wot be's sooper fast) buts normaly we duz only do runnings that sooper fast wen you's about to take ours spot on the sofa.

5. We makes sooper gard dogs (so long as the bergler duz tripping ova our snoozing selfs and nocking themselfs out on sumfing hard).

6. Our furs duz not sniffs like wot uvva dogs duz. Unless you's talking about ours bottoms becoz we can makes sum qwite sooper smells wivs that!

7. We's sooper at helping you wiv the washings hup! You duznt needs a dish washings fing wen you's got a hound.

8. Boy hounds is speshally helpy in the garden wivs waterings the plants. Gerl hounds is qwite sooper at makings sure the grass be's watered.

9. We's sooper qwiet and calm and duz luffs fusses and sosidges. If you's eva got sosidges wot you duznt wants, we can help you gets rid of them.

10. Did I menshon we luffs snoozings?

Being waked hup be's rood!

For hounds:

Here be's a list of the ten most sooper fings about being a 'tired companyon (in no 'ticular order):

1. ~~Sosidges~~
2. ~~Chikin~~
3. ~~Livers~~
4. ~~Bacons~~
5. ~~Cheeze~~

1. Savoury flavouries wot make like raynbows in you's mouf... like sosidges and chikin and livers and bacons and cheeze!

2. Dooveys and blankits and hed cushons and uvva fings wot is like snoozing on clowds!

3. Walkies! Thems not about being empty of poos and wees! Thems about doing sniffings and snufflings and sending wee-mails and chasing sqwirrels!

4. Making noo frends! Wen you's 'tired you sniffs bottoms wivs millyons of noo hounds and makes frends wiv dogs wot is not skinnies wiv pointy noses and sum of thems is even qwite wabbity! I luffs noo frends!

5. Fusses – you get hed fusses and back rubs and tummy fusses all the time!

6. Hadventures! You can goes to the beech or to the woods and you can goes to lundon and you can go on boats and you can hav millyons of

fun on you's hadventures wiv you's noo frends wot you's maked on walkies!

7. Fambly! Having a fambly be's sooper. You's always got sumone to let you out for wees or wot you can go to wen you need hed fusses.

8. Crissmiss! Santa claws and prezants and more savoury flavouries wot makes like raynbows in you's mouf than wot you can possiblies dreem of!

9. Beings snuggled hup in frunt of the fire in winter all rapped hup in you's jarmies.

10. Did I menshon doovey's wot is like clowds and savoury flavouries and walkies and noo frends and fambly and jarmies and crissmiss and hadventures and fusses?

So, if you finks you wood luffs to share you's snoozings place wiv a 'tired afleet, you shood contact you's lowcal greyhound rescoo.

Now if you duz hexcooze meself, I's got more hadventures to do plannings! Being 'tired is sooper!

I luffs sunset walkies!

zzzzz

If you luffed me ritings you can follow me on me blog and me Facebook (I's a very sociable hound)

 **David B M Carr**

@DavidsBestMate

www.davidsbestmate.blogspot.com